SCIENCE

KEY STAGE 2   LEVELS 2–4
TEST A

Page		
2–3		
4–5		
6–7	7	
8–9	6	
10–11	10	
12–13	6	
14–15	3	
16	4	
Total	50	

To do this test you will need a **pencil**, a **ruler**, a **rubber** and a **watch** or **clock** to time yourself.

Sit at a table in a quiet place.

Ask an adult to read through the test instructions with you before you start.

INSTRUCTIONS

1. You will have **45 minutes** to do this test.

2. Read all the words in each question carefully.

3. If you cannot read a word ask an adult to tell you what it says.

4. Use any diagrams or pictures to help you.

5. Try to explain your answers accurately if you are asked to do so.

6. Do not worry if you do not finish all the questions. Do as many as you can.

7. Do not waste time on a question you cannot do. Move quickly on to the next one.

8. Read instructions carefully and write your answers in the spaces highlighted by the handwriting symbols.

9. Move straight on from one page to the next without waiting to be told.

10. If there is time left when you have finished, check your answers and try to do any questions you missed out earlier.

Your first name	
Your last name	

Life processes

 Look at the pictures of these six animals.

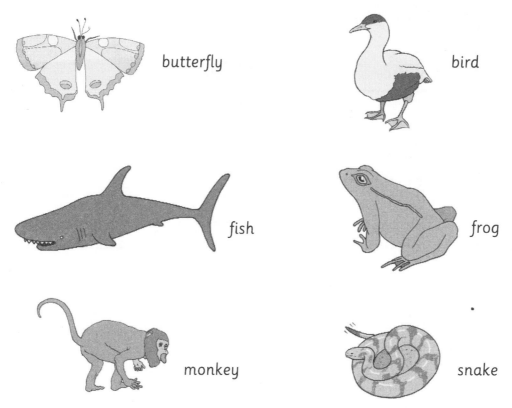

butterfly

bird

fish

frog

monkey

snake

There are some things that all animals do.

All animals spend some of their time feeding.

Write THREE other things that all animals do to stay alive.

a. _____

b. _____

c. _____

Test A

2

Q1a

1 mar

Q1b

1 mar

Q1c

1 mar

Properties of materials

2

a. Which of these things has the smoothest surface?

> carpet   towel   mirror   concrete

_____

b. Circle the TWO objects that a magnet will pick up.

Some things go harder when cooked and some things go softer.

c. What will happen when these things are cooked?
Write their names in the correct place on the chart.

> potato   egg   bread   turnip

Harder	Softer

d. Connect each material to its correct description.

| wool | paper | rubber | cotton | plastic |

Waterproof

Not waterproof

Parents and teachers: Removable instructions and answers are in the centre of the book.

Q2a
1 mark

Q2b
1 mark

Q2c
1 mark

Q2d
1 mark

Electric circuits

3 a. Underline things you need to make a simple electric circuit.

wood   bulb   glass   copper wire

battery   torch   pencil   rubber band

b. Tick **ONE** box for each circuit to show whether the bulb will or will not light.

i

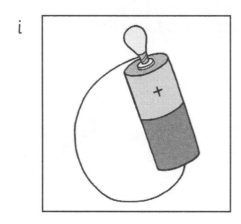

will light   will not light

ii

will light   will not light

iii

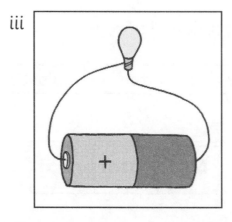

will light   will not light

Plants

4 a. Label the parts of this plant.
Choose from the words in the list.

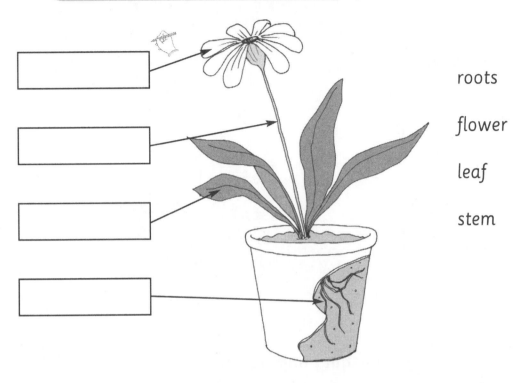

roots

flower

leaf

stem

Q4a

1 mark

Sam and his family are going on holiday for three weeks.
They leave their pot plants indoors with the curtains closed.
When they come back from their holiday the plants are not
growing very well.

b. Give TWO reasons why this is so.

Q4bi

1 mark

i _____

Q4bii

ii _____

1 mark

Parents and teachers: Removable instructions and answers are in the centre of the book.

Melting

 5 Which **TWO** of these materials will melt easily?

Tick **TWO** boxes.

wood ☐   salt ☐

chocolate ☐   wax ☐

stone ☐   brick ☐

Pushing and pulling

 6 Which of these things are usually pushed?
Which of these things are usually pulled?

Write their names in either the box marked PUSH or the box marked PULL.

caravan   pedals   TV button   Christmas cracker
pram   trailer   wheelbarrow   kite on a string

PUSH	**PULL**

Teeth

7 Canines, molars and incisors are the names of different kinds of human teeth.
They do different jobs.

incisor   molar   canines

a. Draw three lines to connect the start of each sentence to its correct ending.

| Canine teeth |
| Molar teeth |
| Incisor teeth |

| bite and cut your food. |
| chew and grind your food. |
| rip and tear your food. |

Q7a

1 mark

b. How many sets of teeth do humans have during their lives?

Q7b

1 mark

_____

c. Tick the suggestions that are useful ways of reducing tooth decay.

eat less sugar ☐   take more exercise ☐

drink more fizzy drinks ☐   use dental floss ☐

brush your teeth thoroughly ☐   eat more vegetables ☐

Q7c

1 mark

Parents and teachers: Removable instructions and answers are in the centre of the book.

Use of materials

8 Some materials are better than others for the job they do.
Look at this labelled drawing of a car.
It shows you what the main parts of the car are made from.

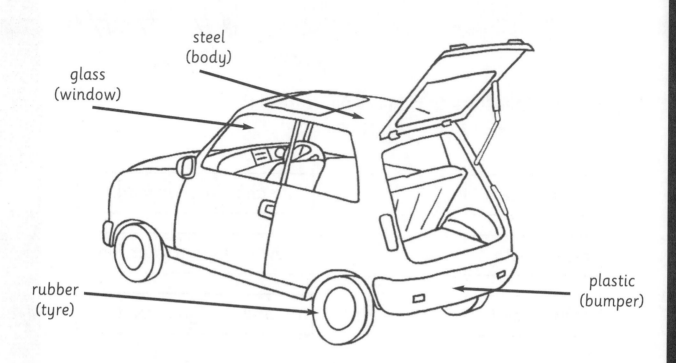

steel
(body)

glass
(window)

rubber
(tyre)

plastic
(bumper)

a. Tick ONE box to show why each
material is right for the job it does.

i The car body is made from steel because it is:

shiny ☐   magnetic ☐   strong ☐

Q8ai

1 mar

ii The car windows are made from glass because it is:

opaque ☐   transparent ☐   brittle ☐

Q8ai

1 mark

iii The car bumpers are made from plastic because it is:

tough ☐   stretchy ☐   heavy ☐

iv The car tyres are made from rubber because it is:

bouncy ☐   flexible ☐   absorbent ☐

Sometimes things are made from a mixture of materials.

b. Draw a line from each object to the pair of materials it is most likely to be made from.

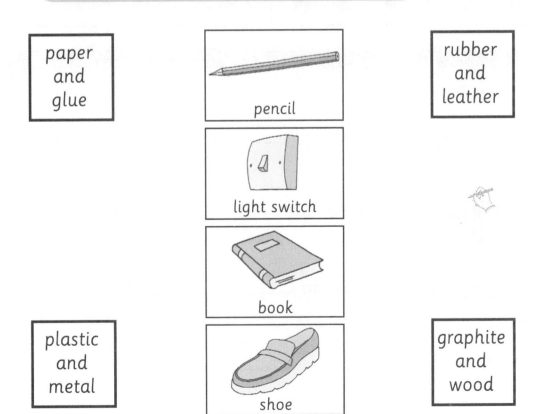

| paper and glue | | rubber and leather |

pencil

light switch

book

shoe

| plastic and metal | | graphite and wood |

Parents and teachers: Removable instructions and answers are in the centre of the book.

Magnets

9 a. Which of these metals will attract a magnet?

Tick **TWO** boxes.

copper ☐   lead ☐

aluminium ☐   iron ☐

brass ☐   steel ☐

Look at each drawing carefully.

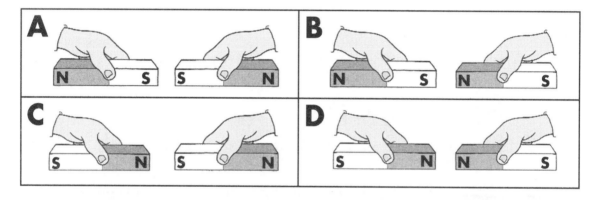

b. Complete the following sentences using either **attract** or **repel**.

i   The magnets in drawing A _____ each other.

ii   The magnets in drawing B _____ each other.

iii The magnets in drawing C _____ each other.

iv   The magnets in drawing D _____ each other.

Pulse rate

 10 Clare takes her pulse rate before she starts running.
She then runs for twenty minutes.
After her run she draws a graph.

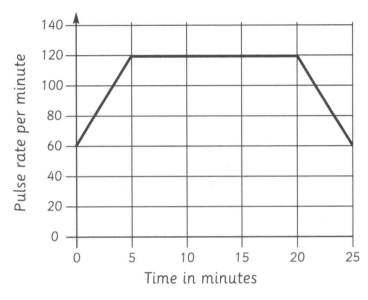

Graph to show
Clare's pulse rate

Use the graph to help you answer these questions.

a. What is Clare's pulse rate:

i before she starts running?

_____ pulses per minute.

ii after fifteen minutes of running?

_____ pulses per minute.

iii five minutes after she stops running?

_____ pulses per minute.

b. What happened to Clare's pulse rate
during the first five minutes of running?

_____

Total

Parents and teachers: Removable instructions and answers are in the centre of the book.

Q10ai

1 mark

Q10aii

1 mark

Q10aiii

1 mark

Q10b

1 mark

Water vapour

These towels have been left to dry.
The water in the towels turns into water vapour in the air.

a. Write the name of the change from water to water vapour.

_____

b. Write the name of the change from water vapour to water.

_____

Shadows

Explain how a shadow is formed.

_____

_____

_____

Q11

1 mar

Q11

1 mar

Q12

1 mar

Circulation

 A group of children did a project on the human heart.

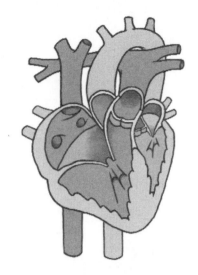

a. What does the heart do to the blood inside the body?

_____

_____

_____

b. The children discovered that blood travels around the body in blood vessels.

i   What is the name of the blood vessels that carry blood away from the heart?

_____

ii What is the name of the blood vessels that carry blood to the heart?

_____

Total

Parents and teachers: Removable instructions and answers are in the centre of the book.

Testing materials

 Donna and Neil tested **sugar**, **sand**, **salt** and **sawdust** to find out which of these materials would dissolve in water.

They filled a jar nearly to the top with water and put one level teaspoon of sugar into the water.

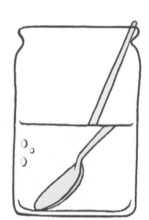

They stirred the sugar and water slowly 50 times and finally looked to see what had happened to the mixture.

They recorded what they saw in the first column on the **table**.

Then they left the mixture to stand for one hour.

They did the experiment three more times: once with sand, once with salt and once with sawdust.

When they had tested all four materials they filled in the final column on the table.
Here are their results.

Material	Appearance after mixing	Appearance after 1 hour
sugar	clear liquid	water looks like clean tap water
sand	particles spinning and gradually falling to the bottom	water clear with all the sand at the bottom
salt	Slightly cloudy looking	clear liquid
sawdust	particles floating about in the mixture and gradually moving upwards	clear water with sawdust floating on the water surface

a. What is the difference between a soluble and an insoluble material?

_____

_____

_____

b. Which of the materials tested by Donna and Neil dissolved in water?

_____

c. Show on the drawings how the mixtures with the sand and the sawdust in them looked after an hour.

Label your additions to each drawing.

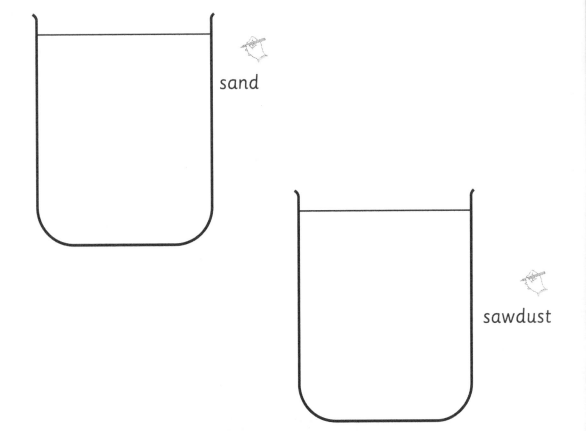

sand

sawdust

a. Draw TWO arrows on the diagram to show the forces acting on the cube of ice floating in the glass of water.

Next to each arrow write the name of the force.

b. Name the force that is slowing this parachutist as he falls through the air.

_____

c. Complete this sentence.

The force that slows things down when they rub together is called

_____

STOP HERE

Total

Q15a

2
mark

Q15b

1 mar

Q15c

1 mark

Have a go! Science Tests

Ages 9–10

Pull-out instructions and answers

Contents

Tests A and B can be found in the main body of the book.

SCIENCE Practice for

Key Stage 2 National Tests

(Levels 2–4)

Introduction for Parents

These practice tests have been compiled to help your child prepare for the National Tests in Science that are taken towards the end of Year 6 at Primary School. The layout of the test material, the marking scheme and the level thresholds closely resemble the 'real' test papers. This means that it is possible, by using Tests A and B, to gain an indication of the National Curriculum level at which your child is working.

Your child should do **Test A** first and then **Test B**.

- ❖ Do each test on a separate day.
- ❖ Choose a time of day when your child is not tired or irritable.
- ❖ Be positive and cheerful before your child begins and give as much encouragement as you can so that they start each test with confidence.
- ❖ Make sure that there are no disturbances while the test is being taken.
- ❖ Go through the instructions on the front page of each test thoroughly with your child before they begin.
- ❖ Answer any questions or queries your child might have about the test instructions.
- ❖ During the test, if your child cannot read a word, you may read it out to them but do not explain its meaning.
- ❖ Make sure your child has a pencil, a ruler, a rubber and a clock or watch to time themselves.
- ❖ Once started, don't fuss and keep looking over your child's shoulder or distract them in any way.

Marking the tests

- ❖ Use the mark schemes provided on pages iii–vi of this booklet and award marks as indicated in the scheme. Use your discretion when marking as some answers may have more than one correct response.
- ❖ In the margin of each test paper, alongside each question, there is a mark box for each question part. In this box write the number of marks scored by your child for that part of the question. If your child gets the question wrong place a '0' in the box. If your child does not attempt the question put a '–' in the box. Do not leave any mark box empty.
- ❖ At the bottom of all right-hand page margins and on the final page of each test is a 'total' box. Fill this in with either the total number of marks scored on the double page spread or, in the case of the last page for each test, the total number of marks for that page. Write each of these totals on the 'marking grid' on the front cover of each test, add them up and fill in the total marks scored in the appropriate space.
- ❖ Transfer this final mark to the correct test column on the first table on page vii of this booklet.

The questions in both Test A and B cover the NC level ranges 2–4.

After you have marked both tests follow the instructions on page vii of this booklet to work out your child's National Curriculum Level. Remember, these are only practice tests and the results obtained by your child should be interpreted as guidance only.

Answers to Test A

Q			Marks
1	a. b. c.	Award 1 mark for each correct response chosen from the answers below to a maximum of 3 marks: breathe (respire) grow excrete (go to the toilet) rest (sleep) breed (reproduce, have young, have babies) use their senses Do not credit a mark for feed (GIVEN), drink, or eat (included under feeding), see, hear, talk, swim, fly, live or feed their young.	3
2	a. b.	mirror Circled: paper clip and bulldog clip Do not credit a mark if more than 2 objects are circled.	1 1

Harder	Softer
egg bread	potato turnip

	c.		1
	d.	WATERPROOF - rubber, plastic NOT WATERPROOF - wool, paper, cotton	1
3	a.	Underlined: bulb, copper wire, battery Do not credit a mark if more than three words are underlined.	1
	b.	i Ticked: will light ii Ticked: will not light iii Ticked: will light Do not credit a mark for a part if both boxes are ticked.	1 1 1

4	a.	flower / stem / leaf / roots	1
	b.	i and ii: Award 1 mark for each of the following reasons to a maximum of 2 marks: not enough light/sun not enough water/no water not enough warmth/not warm enough	2

5	Award 1 mark for each of: chocolate ✓ wax ✓ If more than two boxes are ticked, deduct 1 mark for each incorrect answer.	2

6	Award 1 mark for each correctly filled box. PUSH: pedals, TV button, pram, wheelbarrow PULL: caravan, Christmas cracker, trailer, kite on a string.	2

Q			Marks
7	a.	Award 1 mark for all three sentence starts correctly connected: Canine teeth → rip and tear your food. Molar teeth → chew and grind your food. Incisor teeth → bite and cut your food.	1
	b.	2 (two)	1
	c.	Award 1 mark if all three boxes are ticked correctly. eat less sugar ✓ use dental floss ✓ brush your teeth thoroughly ✓ Do not give credit if more than three boxes are ticked.	1
8	a.	Award 1 mark for each correct section to a maximum of 4 marks. i strong ✓ ii transparent ✓ iii tough ✓ iv flexible ✓ Do not give credit if more than one box is ticked in any section.	4
	b.	Award 1 mark for any two objects joined to what they are made from, to a maximum of 2 marks. paper and glue pencil light switch book shoe rubber and leather plastic and metal graphite and wood	2
9	a.	Award 1 mark for each of: iron ✓ steel ✓ Do not give credit if more than two boxes are ticked.	2
	b.	Award 1 mark for each correct section to a maximum of 4 marks. i repel ii attract iii attract iv repel	4

Q			Marks
10	a.	Award 1 mark for each correct section to a maximum of 3 marks.	3
	i	60 pulses per minute	
	ii	120 pulses per minute	
	iii	60 pulses per minute	
	b.	Award 1 mark for an indication that his pulse rate increased. Accept any of these responses: it went up/rose it got bigger/higher/faster it went up quickly it doubled	1
11	a.	Award 1 mark for: evaporation (or other forms of this word eg. evaporated, evaporate)	1
	b.	Award 1 mark for: condensation (or other forms of this word eg, condensed, condense)	1
12		Award 1 mark for an awareness that a shadow is formed when the path of light from a light source is blocked by an opaque object (use discretion)	1
13	a.	Award 1 mark for an awareness of the role of the heart in the circulation of blood: the heart pumps/sends/moves/pushes the blood round the body Do not give credit for takes blood round the body.	1
	b.	Award 1 mark for each correct section to a maximum of 2 marks.	2
	i	arteries (artery)	
	ii	veins (vein)	
14	a.	Award 1 mark for an answer that clearly defines the difference in meaning between the two words: A soluble material is one that is able to be dissolved in a liquid but an insoluble material cannot be dissolved in a liquid.	1
	b.	Award 1 mark if both sugar and salt are given for the answer. Do not credit a mark if more than two words are included in the answer.	1

Q			Marks
	c.	Award 1 mark if both drawings clearly show where the undissolved material is to be found. Make sure that each drawing is correctly labelled.	1

Q			Marks
15	a.	Award 1 mark if both arrows are present. One arrow must be pointing upwards and the other must be pointing downwards. Credit the mark if the arrows are at the side of the glass.	1
		Award 1 mark if both forces represented by the arrows are clearly indicated.	1

		Do not give credit for only one arrow or arrows pointing in the wrong direction. Do not give credit if only one force is named.	
	b.	air resistance	1
	c.	friction	1

Answers to Test B

Q			Marks
1	a.	Award 1 mark if all six boxes are labelled correctly.	1

water: liquid ✓
iron: solid ✓
paper: solid ✓
milk: liquid ✓
lemonade: liquid ✓
rock: solid ✓

Do not award a mark if there are more than six ticks.

| | b. | Award 1 mark if all six materials are on the correct row in the table. | 1 |

Natural	slate, wood, stone
Manufactured	plastic, brick, glass

2	a.	Award 1 mark for each correct section to a maximum of 2 marks.	2
	i	Materials such as glass or water would be creditworthy answers.	
	ii	Materials such as wood, brick, stone or metal would be creditworthy answers.	
	b.	Award 1 mark for a tick indicating that it 'reflects light'. Do not give credit if more than one box is ticked.	1
3	a.	Award 1 mark for each for hearing and taste (tasting).	2
	b.	Underlined: help us move our body	1
	c.	Award 1 mark if all the stages are in the correct order. baby, toddler, child, teenager, adult	1
4	a.	bath sponge	1
	b.	Award 1 mark for any three of the following items: paper, leather, pipe cleaner, bath sponge, rubber band	1
	c.	rubber band	1
	d.	7(seven)	1
5	a.	Award 1 mark for each correct section.	3

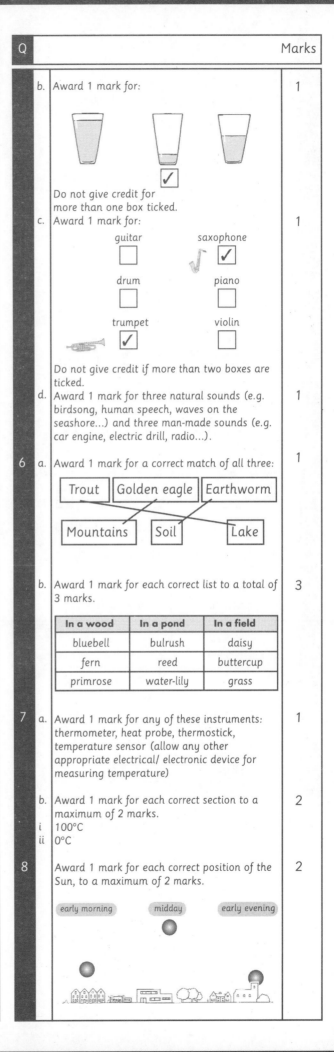

Do not give credit if more than 3 children are circled.

| | b. | Award 1 mark for: | 1 |

Do not give credit for more than one box ticked.

| | c. | Award 1 mark for: | 1 |

guitar ☐   saxophone ✓
drum ☐   piano ☐
trumpet ✓   violin ☐

Do not give credit if more than two boxes are ticked.

| | d. | Award 1 mark for three natural sounds (e.g. birdsong, human speech, waves on the seashore...) and three man-made sounds (e.g. car engine, electric drill, radio...). | 1 |
| 6 | a. | Award 1 mark for a correct match of all three: | 1 |

Trout — Lake
Golden eagle — Mountains
Earthworm — Soil

| | b. | Award 1 mark for each correct list to a total of 3 marks. | 3 |

In a wood	In a pond	In a field
bluebell	bulrush	daisy
fern	reed	buttercup
primrose	water-lily	grass

7	a.	Award 1 mark for any of these instruments: thermometer, heat probe, thermostick, temperature sensor (allow any other appropriate electrical/ electronic device for measuring temperature)	1
	b.	Award 1 mark for each correct section to a maximum of 2 marks.	2
	i	100°C	
	ii	0°C	
8		Award 1 mark for each correct position of the Sun, to a maximum of 2 marks.	2

early morning   midday   early evening

Q			Marks
9	a.	Award 1 mark for any three parts of the skeleton correctly identified to a maximum of 2 marks.	2
		skull — breastbone — ribs — backbone — lower leg bone — kneecap	
	b.	Award 1 mark for each of: protection ✓ health ☐ comfort ☐ growth ☐ speed ☐ support ✓ Do not give credit if more than two boxes are ticked.	2
10	a.	Award 1 mark for each correct section.	2
	i	flexible ☐ heatproof ☐ a conductor ✓	
	ii	an insulator ✓ tough ☐ colourful ☐	
	b.	Award 1 mark if all the materials are in the correct columns.	1

electrical conductor	electrical insulator
tin	cork
silver	paper
aluminium	cotton

Q			Marks
10	c.	TRUE	1
11	a.	gravity	1
	b.	Award 1 mark for all three correct responses. Underlined: water flowing in a river, rain falling, a leaf dropping from a tree Do not give credit if more than three movements are underlined.	1

Q			Marks
12	a.	not smoking	1
	b.	eating less sugar	1
13	a. i	Award 1 mark if both i and ii are correct.	1
		Earth	
	ii	1 day or 24 hours Do not give credit if the numbers are correct but the units are missing.	
	b.	Accept 27-30 days inclusive/1 month/4 weeks	1
	c.	Ticked: Diagram iii	1
		iii.	
14	a.	use a sieve (by sieving)	1
	b.	by filtering the sand from the water using either filter paper or a piece of cloth	1
	c.	it has evaporated	1
	d.	use a magnet weigh each can (steel cans are slightly heavier than aluminium cans) look for rust on each can (steel cans will rust but aluminium cans will not)	1
15	a.	leaf → aphid → ladybird → wren Do not give credit for responses that reverse the order.	1
	b.	leaf	1
	c.	aphid, ladybird, wren (in order)	1

Working Out Your Child's National Curriculum Level

When working out your child's level from the information given on this page it must be remembered that the results obtained from the tests in this book are only a rough guide to your child's likely performance. They will, however, help to give your child valuable test practice and give you an insight into the strengths and weaknesses in their learning. Please remember, this has only been a practice test and the results obtained by your child should be interpreted as guidance only.

Once you have marked both tests enter the total number of marks scored by your child for each test in the appropriate box in the table below.

	TEST A	TEST B	TOTAL
Possible Total	50	50	100
Child's Mark			

Finding the level for Test A or Test B
You can convert your child's score for Test A or Test B into a National Curriculum level by comparing your child's mark against the level thresholds shown on the chart below.

Chart to Show Your Child's National Curriculum Level for Test A or Test B				
	Below Level 2	Level 2	Level 3	Level 4
Marks	0–8	9–25	26–41	42+

Finding the overall level for both tests
Use the chart below and your child's total marks for the two tests to work out his or her overall level for science. **The target level for 9–10 year olds in Year 5 at Primary School is the upper half of the mark range for Level 3.** When interpreting your child's level, be aware that there is quite a wide range for each level. Check to see if your child has just gained a level, is in the middle of the mark range or has just missed a level by a mark or two.

Chart to Show Your Child's Overall National Curriculum Level				
	Below Level 2	Level 2	Level 3	Level 4
Marks	0–16	17–50	51–82	83+

Vocabulary Your Child Should Know

The word lists on the next page contain key vocabulary for science at Key Stage 2. Each list is made up of words that frequently occur in Key Stage 2 SATs. Learning the correct spelling and meaning of each word is important for the success of your child.
The words have been arranged in groups of ten for ease of learning. The two tick boxes after each word are there for you or your child to record progress. Put a tick in the first box when your child understands the scientific meaning of the word and a tick in the second box when your child can spell the word correctly. The word groups on the top half of the page are easier than those on the bottom half of the page.

Key Vocabulary
Easier words

warm-blooded	vibrate	fair test	stretch
solid	melt	repel	sieve
gravity	food chain	axis	incisor
predict	freeze	milk teeth	anther
petal	attract	soak	filter
liquid	record	mixture	force
stigma	pulse	molar	style
gas	soluble	boil	mass
stamen	muscle	push	prey
steam	affect	result	absorb

key	stem	reflect	brain
shadow	volume	lungs	rotate
mammal	seed	nectar	safe
carpel	habitat	baby	explain
oxygen	orbit	spin	process
root	describe	diagram	weight
leaf	skeleton	feature	heart
pull	support	child	canine
reason	pitch	adult	cold-blooded
flower	idea	teenager	gram (g)

Key Vocabulary
Harder words

producer	information	predator	mineral
transparent	air resistance	material	condensation
circuit	condense	magnetic force	absorbent
investigate	consumer	pattern	pollination
microbe	photosynthesis	increase	waterproof
solution	water vapour	water cycle	magnetic
evaporate	upthrust	diaphragm	property
preserve	evidence	complete	seed dispersal
friction	nutrient	organism	protection
measure	reflection	conductor	permeable

thermometer	non-magnetic	circulation	fertilisation
newton (N)	combustion	flammable	dangerous
germinate	nutrition	loudness	germination
evaporation	movement	function	prediction
forcemeter	dissolve	investigation	closed switch
vibration	decrease	open switch	irreversible
carbohydrate	experiment	reversible	symbol
temperature	periscope	environment	luminous
plaque	impermeable	translucent	flexible
saturate	moisture	rotation	opaque

SCIENCE

KEY STAGE 2   LEVELS 2–4
TEST B

Marking Grid		
Page	Marks possible	Marks scored
18–19	5	
20–21	8	
22–23	6	
24–25	9	
26–27	8	
28–29	7	
30–31	4	
32	3	
Total	50	

To do this test you will need a **pencil**, a **ruler**, a **rubber** and a **watch** or **clock** to time yourself.

Sit at a table in a quiet place.

Ask an adult to read through the test instructions with you before you start.

INSTRUCTIONS

1. You will have **45 minutes** to do this test.

2. Read all the words in each question carefully.

3. If you cannot read a word ask an adult to tell you what it says.

4. Use any diagrams or pictures to help you.

5. Try to explain your answers accurately if you are asked to do so.

6. Do not worry if you do not finish all the questions. Do as many as you can.

7. Do not waste time on a question you cannot do. Move quickly on to the next one.

8. Read instructions carefully and write your answers in the spaces highlighted by the handwriting symbols.

9. Move straight on from one page to the next without waiting to be told.

10. If there is time left when you have finished, check your answers and try to do any questions you missed out earlier.

Your first name	
Your last name	

Grouping materials

1 a. Which of these are solid? Which of these are liquid?

Tick the right boxes.

water
solid | liquid
☐ | ☐

iron
solid | liquid
☐ | ☐

paper
solid | liquid
☐ | ☐

milk
solid | liquid
☐ | ☐

rock
solid | liquid
☐ | ☐

lemonade
solid | liquid
☐ | ☐

Q1a

1 mark

Some materials in this house are natural.
Some have to be manufactured.

b. Write the name of each material on the correct row in the table.

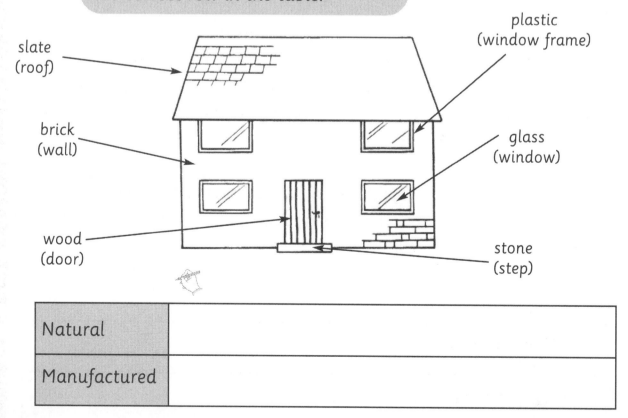

slate
(roof)

plastic
(window frame)

brick
(wall)

glass
(window)

wood
(door)

stone
(step)

Natural	
Manufactured	

Q1b

1 mark

Light

2 a. Transparent materials let light pass through them.
   Opaque materials do not let light pass through them.

   i  Write the name of ONE transparent material.

   _____

   ii Write the name of ONE opaque material.

   _____

b. This pan looks shiny.

   Why does the pan look shiny? Tick ONE box.

   It is curved.

   It gives out light.

   Light passes through it.

   It reflects light.

Q2ai

1 mark

Q2aii

1 mark

Q2b

1 mark

Total

Humans

3 You have FIVE senses. Three of them are given here.

> sight   smell   touch

a. Write the names of the other **TWO** senses.

_____   _____

b. Underline the best ending for this sentence.

Muscles are used to...

make us fit and healthy.

hold our body together.

help us move our body.

Throughout your life you go through FIVE different stages.
The stages are shown below.

baby   teenager   toddler   adult   child

c. Write the FIVE stages in the correct order.
Start with the baby.

_____

Changing shape

 4 Sarah and Amjad tested eight items to find out which items will bend, twist, stretch and squash.

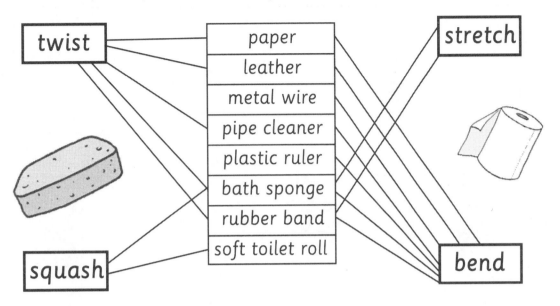

Use their results to help you answer the following questions.

a. Which item will bend, twist, stretch and squash?

_____

b. Name THREE items that will twist.

_____

c. Write the name of the missing item in this sentence.

The _____ will stretch, twist and bend.

d. How many of the items tested by Sarah and Amjad will bend?

_____

5 **a.** Circle the child in each picture who will hear the loudest barking.

i

ii

iii

Q5ai

1 mark

Q5aii

1 mark

Q5aiii

1 mark

b. Tick the glass that will make the highest sound if you hit it with a spoon.

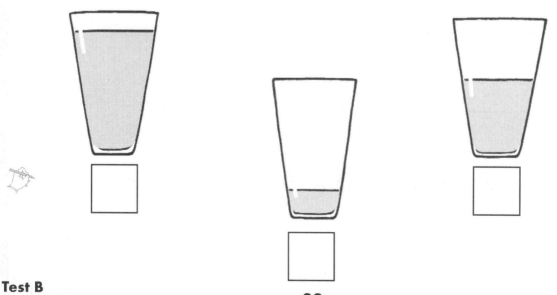

Q5b

1 mark

There are many kinds of sounds and things that make sounds. Look at the pictures of these musical instruments.

c. Tick the ones that we blow to make a sound.

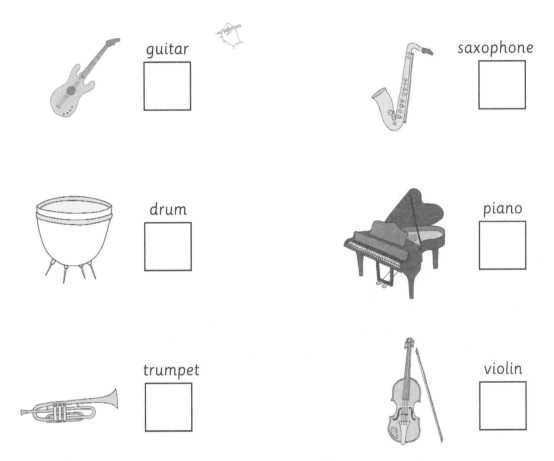

guitar ☐

saxophone ☐

drum ☐

piano ☐

trumpet ☐

violin ☐

Some sounds are natural.
Some are man-made.

d. Write the names of THREE different sounds in each column on the chart.

natural sounds	man-made sounds

Total

Parents and teachers: Removable instructions and answers are in the centre of the book.

Q5c
1 mark

Q5d
1 mark

Living things in their environments

6 a. Draw THREE lines to connect each animal to the place where it lives.

Trout

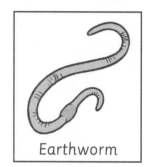
Golden eagle

Earthworm

b. Where are each of these plants usually found?
Write them in the correct list.
Each list should contain THREE plants.

daisy   bluebell   bulrush

reed   fern   buttercup

primrose   grass   water-lily

In a wood	In a pond	In a field

Temperature

7 Temperature is a measure of how hot or cold something is.

a. Write the name of the instrument that is used to measure temperature.

_____

b. Temperature is usually measured in degrees Celsius (°C).

i At what temperature does water normally boil?

_____

ii At what temperature does water normally freeze?

_____

The sun

8 This picture shows the position of the sun in the sky in the early morning.

On the picture, draw the sun in the correct position below each time heading.

early morning   midday   early evening

Parents and teachers: Removable instructions and answers are in the centre of the book.

Q7a
1 mark

Q7bi
1 mark

Q7bii
1 mark

Q8
2 marks

The human skeleton

 Look at this drawing of a human skeleton.

a. Connect the name of each part with its position on the skeleton.

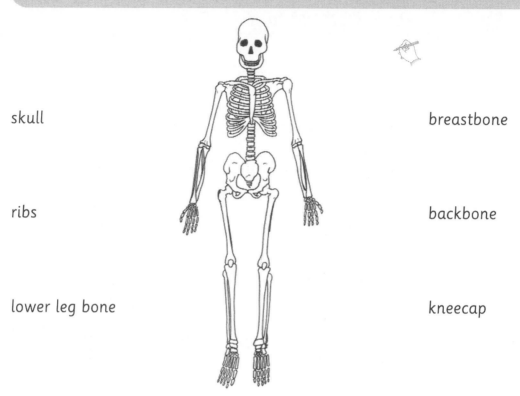

skull

ribs

lower leg bone

breastbone

backbone

kneecap

Your skeleton allows your body to move.

b. Which TWO other important features does the skeleton provide for the human body?

Tick TWO boxes.

protection ☐   health ☐

comfort ☐   growth ☐

speed ☐   support ☐

Electricity

10 a. Electrical wires are made from copper.

i

Copper is

flexible ☐   heatproof ☐   a conductor ☐

Electrical wires are covered with plastic.

ii Tick ONE box to explain why this is so.

Plastic is

an insulator ☐   tough ☐   colourful ☐

b. Write each material in the correct column on the chart.

electrical conductor	electrical insulator

cork   tin   paper   silver   cotton   aluminium

c. Write TRUE or FALSE after reading the statement below.

Electricity can pass through most metals. _____

Test A

27

Total

Q10ai
1 mark

Q10aii
1 mark

Q10b
1 mark

Q10c
1 mark

Parents and teachers: Removable instructions and answers are in the centre of the book.

Forces

 11 a. Write the name of the pulling force
which makes objects fall to the ground.

_____

b. Underline the movements listed below that happen
because of the force you have named in part a.

water flowing in a river   smoke rising

a ship sailing   rain falling

flowers growing   a leaf dropping from a tree

Health

 12 Complete the statements below by writing
the TWO correct phrases from the list.

One has been done for you.

not smoking	taking more exercise
washing your hands	eating less sugar

Reduce your chance of food poisoning by <u>washing your hands</u>.

a. Reduce your risk of lung cancer by

_____.

b. Reduce your risk of tooth decay by

_____.

Q11a

1 mark

Q11b

1 mark

Q12a

1 mark

Q12b

1 mark

Sun, Earth and Moon

13 a. Here is a diagram showing the Earth orbiting the Sun.

Sun

Earth

not to scale

i On the diagram, draw a line to show the axis of the Earth.

ii How long does it take the Earth to make one complete rotation on its axis?

_____

b. How long does it take the moon to orbit the Earth?

_____

c. Tick the diagram that shows an eclipse of the Sun.

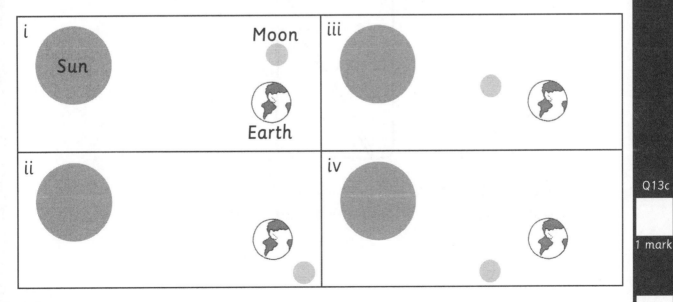

i Sun   Moon

Earth

iii

ii

iv

Q13a

1 mark

Q13b

1 mark

Q13c

1 mark

Parents and teachers: Removable instructions and answers are in the centre of the book.

Separating mixtures

Terry's granny put some cornflakes in a bowl. Before she poured on some milk, Terry sprinkled sugar on the cornflakes. But Terry's granny did not like sugar on her cornflakes so she asked him to separate the sugar from the cornflakes.

a. What is the easiest way for Terry to separate the large cornflake particles from the sugar?

Q14a

1 mark

_____

This beaker contains water and sand which has just been stirred.

b. How could you quickly separate the grains of sand from the water?

Q14b

1 mark

_____

This beaker contains a solution of salt and water.
It is left in a warm room.
After 1 week all that remains in the beaker is salt.

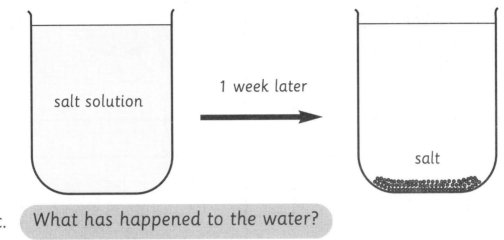

salt solution

1 week later

salt

c. What has happened to the water?

_____

Sally has a pile of ten empty metal drink cans.
Some cans are made of aluminium and some are made of steel.

d. What method can Sally use to quickly separate the
aluminium cans from the steel cans?

_____

Total

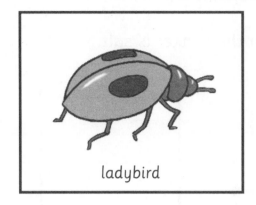

ladybird

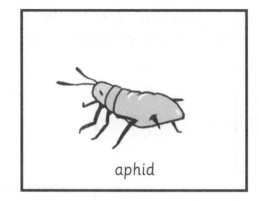

aphid

wren

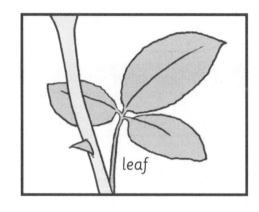

leaf

Aphids eat leaves.
Wrens eat ladybirds.
Ladybirds eat aphids.

a. Write this as a food chain.

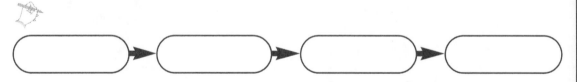

Q15a

1 mark

b. Write the name of the producer in this food chain.

_____

Q15b

1 mark

c. Write the name of the consumers in this food chain.

Q15c

_____

1 mark

STOP HERE

Test B

Total